HABITS OF HIGHLY EFFECTIVE CHRISTIANS

BIBLE STUDY GUIDE

BY RON MEYERS

Ronald R. Meyers
4422 E. 82nd Street
Tulsa OK, 74137

www.xulonpress.com

Contents

———⟫•0•⟪———

Introduction

————⟫•◦⟨◦•⟨————

*Y*ou are the main character in this book. This book is about you, your life, your growth, your dreams, and your plan of action to see God's dream for you materialize. By the time you are through with this book your responses, ideas, and goals will be on every page. The questions are designed to help you think through your personal plan for growth based on what you learned in *Habits of Highly Effective Christians* and your Bible. After you have completed this book you will be yet another big step toward knowing how to become your best possible self.

Do not hurry this process. Don't be afraid to contemplate at length before you write your responses. You may even leave some blanks empty without responding immediately—giving you an opportunity to mull things over before you respond. Make your answers as long or as brief as you like. The important thing is that you interact personally with the ideas and allow God to speak to you through His Word.

This is a thematic Bible Study with subjects organized around the life-related biblical ideas found in *Habits of Highly Effective Christians*. This is not a study of *Habits of Highly Effective Christians*; it is a study of the Bible using subjects raised in *Habits of Highly Effective Christians*. By the time you have worked your way through this book, you and your Bible will be better friends. Your value system and outlook on life will become more and more closely aligned with God's Word; you will be richer in character and wiser in handling life's challenges.

HABIT ONE

Learn From Experience

---

1. A high percentage of the Bible is narrative—stories of human experiences. What does that say about God's view of one person learning from the experience of another?

   _____

   What are your thoughts on this subject? _____

   _____

   _____

2. Do you think you have learned things through your own experience? _____

   Can you list three important lessons you have learned by experience? _____

   _____

   _____

   _____

   What experience(s) have you had from which you might have, but did not learn? _____

   _____

   Is it too late to learn from it now? _____

3. What caution would you give to someone who has supposedly "learned" something through experience, but what they "learned" doesn't accord with Scripture?_____

   _____

   What do you think people should do to prevent themselves from learning amiss through experience? _____

   _____

4. What leader or example have you learned from by just watching that person's life?

_____

Did they intentionally "teach" you or did you just learn by observing? _____

5. What advantages can you think of that belong to persons who can learn from experiences while they are still having the experiences? _____

_____

What change in your attitude might be required so you become able to make life's experiences learning opportunities? _____

Consider what way your complaints about life's circumstances hindered you from learning from part of your experience. _____

_____

_____

6. Was it a surprise to you that God is so intricately involved in each detail of your life as is suggested by Acts 17:26? _____

If God intentionally had you born in a specific family, time, and place, what reinterpretation of your family setting do you need to do? _____

_____

How will that help you begin to see what God may intend to do with you or how He may want to use your life?_____

_____

7. Were you disappointed in the way you began your race? _____ How? _____

_____

What can you begin to do now to try to make sure you end your race well? _____

_____

_____

8. Look up Proverbs 19:2, Romans 10:2 and Galatians 4:18 and make a brief comparison

between zeal and wisdom._____

_____

What did you learn in this chapter about the comparative importance of zeal and

wisdom?_____

Which is more important to the person who wants to end well, zeal or wisdom? _____

_____

What will you need to begin to do differently as a result of your discovery?_____

_____

9. Identify two Bible characters that had to wait a long time for their lives to begin to count

for God in a significant way? _____ What was the outcome of their

waiting in each of these cases? _____

_____

Do their examples, or the outcome of their lives, encourage you? _____

How? _____

_____

10. What have you learned from your parent's examples? _____

_____

What did you observe about your parents that you do not want to copy? _____

_____

11. What do you need to do to increase your spiritual authority—your ability to influence

others spiritually? _____

_____

Are you yielding to the "hammer and chisel"—people—God is using to chip away the

character flaws in your life? _____

_____ Do you become angry with the "hammer and

chisel"—people—God is using in your life?_____

Are there ways you can change that? _____

_____

12. What people in your sphere of influence can or should you begin to influence by your

    godly example and spiritual authority? _____

    _____

    How has your attitude hindered your influence in the past? _____

    _____

    How can you change that?_____

    _____

13. How is I Corinthians 10:13 a guarantee that we will pass every test?_____

    _____

    How does this add to your confidence?_____

14. Write down an example of a prayer that God answered for you when you were young, or

    a young Christian?_____

    In what way has that influenced your attitude toward prayer? _____

    _____

    Can you see any connections between what you learned about prayer then and what God

    later taught you or did through you? _____

    _____

15. How does Luke 16:10 demonstrate the connection between our character and behavior—

    being and doing?_____

    _____

    What connection do you see between "little" and "big" decisions?" _____

    _____

16. What experience have you had through which you discovered that something good in

    itself, even something God had given to you, had become more important to you than

God? _____

How can you avoid such pitfalls in the future? _____

How is it that things God gives to us become "gods" or "idols?"_____

_____

Are such "gods" or "idols" included in God's instructions found in Exodus 20:3 & 4?

_____

_____

17. Think of a way in which Philippians 1:6 could be an encouragement to someone involved in a difficult learning experience. _____

_____

When was that verse and biblical principle helpful to you? _____

How? _____

18. What help is it to us in a difficult learning experience when we recall there is a bigger picture and that God has a noble, eternal, and lofty goal for our future? _____

_____

How can we become more content with our present lot in life when we "see" the eternal dimension?_____

What will help us mature so that we will be more willing to know that our hopes will be eventually gratified, even if they are delayed? _____

_____

19. What was the most important lesson you learned from this chapter?_____

_____

What new goal would you like to set for yourself based upon your reflections on this chapter? _____

_____

HABIT TWO

Recognize Learning Opportunities

———➤•◄———

1. Do you remember when you discovered that you had a unique one-to-one relationship with God? _____ How old were you? _____ How has it affected you since then? _____

   _____

2. What specific incidence in your life as a child gave you the impression you were unique? _____ Do you know the meaning of your name?_____ What is it? _____ Does knowing that affect your relationship with God or your efforts to please Him? _____Were there any miracles in your life as a child that taught you, or that now upon reflection teach you, that God has individual and special interest in you? _____

   _____

3. Did you ever have a brush with death? _____When and what were the circumstances? _____ What was your interpretation of that event then? _____ As you reflect now on that event, what is your interpretation? _____

   _____

4. Read Ps. 139:13-16, Jer. 1:5, and Acts 17:26. What about the way God formed you do you like? _____ What things about the way God formed you do you dislike? _____

   Do you need to rethink any of this in view of the fact that God was intentional about those details? _____

_____

5. Is there anyone in your circle of life activities that you have failed to recognize was one of God's "agents" for your development? _____ How can you rethink your relationship with them in view of the possibility that God intentionally placed them in your life? _____

_____

_____

6. Has there been any abusive person in your life? _____ Did their abuse— physical or verbal—permanently affect you? _____ Have you forgiven them? _____ How could you now reinterpret that past experience to see how God can use bad things bad people do to us to develop us—without blaming God for the bad the enemy intended for us? _____

_____

7. In view of Ps 139:13-16, Jer. 1:5, and Acts 17:26, which we read above, what skills did God create in you?_____

_____

In what way does that skill hint what God may want you to do with your life?_____

_____

_____

8. Read Mt. 5:37 and James 5:12. We have defined integrity as having your thoughts, words, and actions integrated. What opportunities have you had lately to prove to yourself, in ways that no one else would know about, that you have integrity? _____

_____

How was God at work in such events, developing you? _____

_____

9. Read I Kings 19:9-18, the famous passage about Elijah hearing the still small voice of God. Has God has spoken to you lately in His still, small, inner voice? _____ What did He say? _____ Did you listen? _____ Was it difficult to hear that voice over the loud clamoring of other voices around you? _____ How do you plan to cultivate the ability to hear the still, small voice of God?_____ _____ Why is this important to you? _____

   _____

10. Read Mat 25:21. What opportunities to serve have you recently experienced that, upon reflection, seems related to your successful fulfillment of an earlier, simpler assignment you faithfully completed? _____

   _____

   Can you see how God might use your present assignments to prepare you for the next ones? _____

11. Hebrews 11 provides a record of trials and victories of faith. Write down a past test of your faith the Lord used to prepare you for further tests. _____

   _____

   _____

   What test of faith have you experienced recently that is part of your continuing preparation?_____

   _____

12. Read Gal. 6:6. The Bible seems to support formal training and payment of tuition. What formal training for Christian work have you had?_____ _____ What formal training are you praying about receiving? _____ How do you think formal training might enhance your experience? _____

   _____

13. Read Rom. 12:3-8, I Cor. 12:1-11, and Eph. 4:11-13. In addition to the gifts listed in those three places, intercession—the ability to travail in prayer—and missionary—the ability to use other gifts in a crosscultural situation—have been suggested as other spiritual gifts. What other possible spiritual gifts or abilities can you think of? _____

_____

_____

What spiritual gifts do you have? _____What have you done to try to discover or develop your spiritual gifts? _____

_____

14. Read Acts 9:26-30, 11:25-29, 12:24,25, and 13:1-4. What ways can you see God used Barnabas to be a mentor for Saul (who became Paul)? _____

_____ What mentor(s) has God used in your life? _____

_____ For whom have you served as a mentor? _____

_____

15. Read the first chapter of Daniel. What geo-political issue did God use to place Daniel and his three friends in a unique crosscultural ministry opportunity?_____

_____

Can you think of either a political, national, or regional situation that has affected your development? _____ Can you think of a situation that you did not allow to develop you—which you now realize could have been a developmental learning experience? _____

_____

16. Read Genesis 32:1 & 22-32. How did Jacob's experience with heavenly beings change his perspective? _____ As you contemplate Jacob's subsequent attitude and behavior toward his brother Esau, what paradigm shift—major change in

perspective—do you see in Jacob's life? _____ What shift in paradigm have you experienced as a result of either prayer or something the Lord specifically showed you?_____

_____

17. Read Eph. 6:10-18. What benefit is there is knowing that unseen forces sometimes work through visible persons? _____ What experiences have you had in which you knew the enemy was at work behind the scenes? _____

How do you advise Christian warriors to view the spiritual forces and the human personalities through whom they sometimes operate? _____

_____

_____

18. Read Rom. 8:28. How did God use an assignment you experienced while completing a ministry or career assignment, to develop you in a special way? _____

_____

_____

How did God use a unique mishap you experienced while completing a ministry or career assignment, to develop you in a special way? _____

_____

What did you discern or learn at the time? _____

_____ After reflection, what do you "see" more clearly? _____

19. Read Ps. 46:10. Write down your thoughts regarding a time of isolation in which God has given you an opportunity to learn something new from Him. _____

_____

_____

What did you learn?_____

20. Read Eph. 4:32 and I Peter 3:8-14. Write down an experience you had in which someone misunderstood you or treated you unfairly. How did (or do) you forgive that person?

_____

What did you learn from that experience?_____

21. What was the most meaningful concept you learned in this chapter?_____

What do you expect to do differently in the future as a result? _____

_____

_____

HABIT THREE

Exercise Self-control

———➤•◆•◄———

1. Read Gal. 5:22,23 and Acts 24:25. Why do you think self-control is a less popular subject than the other fruit of the Spirit listed in those verses?_____

   _____

   _____

   What teaching or preaching on self-control really motivated you to seek this fruit? _____

   _____

2. Read I Cor. 6:19,20 and 9:24-27. Explain how Paul understood the relationship between running life's race well and controlling his bodily appetites? _____

   _____

   Do you feel Paul over-stated his case? _____ Why or why not? _____

   _____

   _____

3. Read Rom 7:14-25, II Cor. 10:3-5, and Gal. 5: 16-18. How do you think controlling our thoughts is like a spiritual "war"? _____

   _____

   What do you do when you lose a battle in this war? _____

   _____

   What precaution would increase the victories in this war?_____

   _____

4. Read Job 31:1. How do you think Job's principle of a "covenant" with his eyes is an

effective weapon for your battles to keep your mind pure? _____

_____

_____

Describe the connection between what we let our eyes see and what we let our minds

think. _____ How could this understanding help us in

the battle for control of our own minds? _____

_____

5. Have you ever fasted? _____ Did you find it beneficial? _____

How? _____

Is readiness to fast an important value to you? _____ How do eating habits set

people up for a more difficult time in fasting than fasting actually requires?_____

_____ Describe your views on the relationship between being ready

to fast and actually fasting. _____

_____

_____

6. What minor step in the direction of self-control do you intend to take toward a more

ordered and fruitful Christian life? _____

Have you ever met a Christian with self-control who regretted having this fruit in their

lives? _____

Describe the beauty of self-control in another's life. _____

_____

How could you show that same beauty in your life?_____

7. Read Mark 14:32-38. Does the rhetorical question Jesus asked His disciple also need a

response from you: "Could you not keep watch for one hour?" _____ What

keeps you from spending regular time in prayer? _____ If you set the amount of

time you intend to pray in advance, do you think you would pray longer than you do now? _____ Would you be willing to undertake a one-month experiment to increase the amount of time you spend in prayer? _____ Record here the date you intend to do this. _____

8. What less valuable activities might you need to cut back on in order to increase the amount of time you pray? _____ Are you willing to give them up?_____ Are you willing to experiment with giving something up for a month in order to pray more and then decide whether you would like to make the change permanent? _____ What would you give up?_____

9. Read Ps. 119 and notice how much David loved God's Word. How can you systematize your Bible reading? _____ Have you ever read the Bible through? _____ Would you like to? _____ How many pages of your Bible would you need to read each day in order to read it through in 365 days? _____

10. What area of your life that was not addressed in this chapter needs to be more controlled? _____ Is there a Christian friend or relative you would like to make yourself accountable to in an effort to bring that area under control? _____ Who is it? _____

11. Have you seen examples of Christians overdoing their self-control or self-discipline? _____ Does their doing something incorrectly, or overdoing it, justify your omitting the discipline altogether? _____ What extremes do you need to be careful to avoid? _____ Do you have a close friend or relative with whom you can discuss how to balance self-control so as to avoid extremes? _____ Who? _____

12. What was the most significant "discovery" for you in this chapter? _____ _____ Will you do anything differently from now on as a result? _____ _____ What? _____ How? _____ _____ What is the desired outcome of the new step you will take? _____

HABIT FOUR

Pray According to God's Agenda

———◦———

1. Have you ever prayed a long time about something only to find out later that God had something entirely different in mind? _____ Have you ever felt the time you spent praying about that concern was wasted? _____ Is it possible that God did you a favor by not answering that prayer? _____

2. Which of the following two qualities do you feel is more important in effective praying: (1) zeal/energy, or (2) wisdom to pray for the right things? _____ What experiences have helped you form this opinion?_____

    _____

3. Have you ever received an answer to prayer that you subsequently wished you had not received? _____ Is it proper to blame God in such instances? _____ How can such problems be avoided in the future? _____

    _____

4. Is there any scriptural guarantee that God always "cancels out" wrong prayers?_____ Even if God did "cancel out" some of our wrong praying, do you feel Christians should try to be responsible to pray prayers they know God Himself really wants to answer? _____ Do you believe Christians have a responsibility to pray, as much as possible, only those things that God wants them to pray for? _____

5. Identify a prayer that God placed in your heart. _____ Did you receive God's answer to that prayer? _____ Describe how that answer brought glory to God. _____

6. Read Nu. 11:10-33 and Ps. 106:13-15. What lesson for us today regarding prayer do you feel the Israelites' experience teaches? _____ What similar experience do you know of wherein someone either married the person, got the job, or bought something they were praying for, but as it turned out, it was not the best for them? _____

_____

_____

7. Read II Kings 20. Was Hezekiah principally concerned about himself or the people in his kingdom? _____ How do you think Hezekiah should have prayed?_____

_____

_____

Does God's answer to Hezekiah's prayer prove that that answer was what God wanted for Hezekiah and Israel at that time? _____ Why or why not?_____

_____

_____

8. Compare Hezekiah's concern for God's reputation demonstrated in II Kings 19:15-19 with his attitude revealed in II Kings 20:19. How can effective Christians avoid becoming selfish or narrow after early successes in life? _____

_____

How do you plan to guard yourself against the dangers of Hezekiah's success? _____

_____

9. How would you have prayed in Hezekiah's situation? _____

_____

How have you prayed in similar situations? _____

Would it be harder to actually accept God's will in a life or death situation than it is to write your response here? _____ What issues are at stake? _____

_____

10. Read I Sam. 23:1-13 and II Sam. 5:17-25. What lesson is to be learned by David's prayer life?_____ How did prayer contribute to David's successful military campaigns? _____ _____Can you name any circumstances in which God said "no" to David's questions? _____ What did David do when God said, "no?" _____

_____

_____

11. Read I Kings chapters 17, 18, and James 5:17 & 18. Why do you think Elijah's prayers were so effective? _____

_____

_____

12. How did you feel when your teacher let you make mistakes and learn from them instead of confronting you with the "right answers" all the time? _____ _____ Did you learn from your experiences with that teacher? _____ Do you believe God sometimes gives us what we want, even when it was not what He wanted, so that we could learn to pray responsibly? _____ Why or why not? _____

_____

_____

13. Read Luke 22:39-44. What lessons about submission in prayer can we learn from Jesus' experience on the Mount of Olives? _____
If you don't know for sure how to pray, or if you are struggling with submitting to something God wants you to do or not to do, what advantage is it to use the phrase, "not my will but yours be done?" _____

_____

14. To carry the above idea to another level, what about your becoming more responsible to

actually pray for the right thing and not rely so much on the safety mechanism of adding "not my will but yours be done?" _____

_____

_____

While "safe," would praying "not my will but yours be done" always be the most effective way to receive specific answers to prayer? _____Why or why not? _____

_____

_____

15. Describe an experience in which God gave you a better answer than the prayer you prayed? _____

_____

_____

_____

16. What advice would you give to someone who was praying for something specific? _____ Do you feel your experience and illustrations will be enough to convince them to be careful how they pray? _____ Why or why not? _____

_____

17. Do you have a friend or confidant to whom you could tell your innermost secret prayers in order to confirm whether it was right to pray as you are? _____ What other "safety mechanism" can you think of to help you avoid praying for the wrong thing?

_____

18. Read Isaiah 55:9 and Eph. 3:20. In view of those verses, what steps will you take to tap into God's wisdom when you pray? _____

_____

How do you plan to avoid praying narrow prayers? _____

_____

19. What was the most helpful discovery about prayer you learned in this chapter? _____

_____

_____

Could your friends also benefit from knowing it? _____

HABIT FIVE

Fast Systematically

---

1. Have you ever told God you would do anything, go anywhere, or say anything for Him? _____ Did you mean it? _____ What if His Spirit nudged you to begin fasting? Are you open to that?_____

2. In order to learn how do big things, are you willing to begin with little things? _____ Does starting with short fasts and progressing to longer fasts make sense to you? _____ Do you feel this is a practical way to get started? _____ How important is fasting in the Christian life? _____ How important is it to you? _____ _____

3. What do you need to do to be ready to systematically fast short lengths of time? _____ Have you ever thought you would like to have the spiritual power that belongs to those who discipline themselves with fasting? _____ What if God were to call you to a long fast? What would you do to prepare? _____ _____

4. Have you been afraid to fast in the past? _____ Do you feel fasting is important enough that our usual eating patterns should be controlled so as to make fasting doable? _____ Is spiritual discipline and growth that important to you?_____

5. Refer to Luke 4:1-2, Acts 9:9, and Dan. 10:3 if necessary. Record your understanding of a normal fast: _____ An absolute fast: _____ A partial fast: _____

6. How did Jesus encourage fasting? _____ Read Mat.

6:18. What did He say about rewards for fasting?_____

_____

Read Mat. 9:15. What did He say about the time period in which fasting would be appropriate? _____ Discuss whether you think that includes now? _____

7. Read Luke 18:11&12. Write down your understanding of the appropriate motive for fasting. _____ Why do you think Jesus encouraged secret fasting? _____ How do you react to people boasting about fasting, prayer, or giving? _____

_____

8. Have you had experience in which God called you to fast? _____ How did God let you know this is what God wanted you to do?_____

_____

_____

9. Do you believe fasting is good for our health? _____ What do you think about fasting for your health?_____ Is that reason enough to fast? _____ Is it possible for us to fast "as unto God" and still experience the physical and health benefits of fasting? _____

_____

10. Read Deut. 8:3, 12-14 and Ezra 8:21& 23. Comment on issues of pride and humility as they are affected by fasting._____ _____ Can you think of a time in your life when fasting aided you in your effort to humble yourself before God? _____ What were the results of that time of fasting and humiliation?_____

_____

11. We all rejoice to hear testimonies of deliverances from bad habits and various forms of

spiritual oppression. In view of the recent rise of occult activity, even in America, the stakes are higher in the war between the forces of righteousness and the forces of darkness. Read Luke 4:18 & 19 and Acts 8:13 - 23, then write down your thoughts on the matter of fasting and spiritual warfare. _____

_____

_____

_____

12. Read Dan. 9:3 & 22 and Acts 10:10. Compare II Cor. 11:27 with II Cor. 12:1. What do you believe about the relationship between fasting and God revealing things to His people? _____ Have you ever experienced a personal revelation? _____ Do you believe God can give personal direction to people today? _____ Why or how does He do this?_____

_____

_____

13. Read Est. 4: 12 – 17. What do you think about fasting when you have a crisis? _____ Do you think it is correct to fast and pray specifically for direction/guidance in a decision? _____ Is direction/guidance a kind of revelation? _____ Why or why not? _____

_____

14. The Bible teaches systematic giving and systematic praying. What do you feel about systematizing spiritual disciplines like fasting and prayer? _____ Can spiritual things remain spiritual when done systematically? _____ Paul said he had "often gone without food." Could part of that have been due to systematic fasting? _____

15. Compare the first time you fasted with later periods of fasting. Do you feel you have made progress? _____ Is your body better able to handle temporary times without food? _____ How would you encourage an inexperienced Christian to

begin to fast? _____ Have you ever introduced this discipline with its great

benefits to another Christian? _____

16. Does God require anything of us that is not good for us? _____ If a person is not

healthy, should they fast? _____ What kinds of unhealthy issues could actually be

relieved through fasting? _____ What kinds of health concerns

should cause us to not fast? _____

_____

17. Have you ever felt that there was no possible way for you to solve your problems?

_____ Do you feel that there are times in Christian's lives in which we must turn

completely to God—that there is no human solution to the problem, that only God can

solve this one? _____ Describe a time in your life when you were in an

impossible situation. _____ Did you fast and pray? _____ If you

had it to do over again, what would you do differently? _____

_____

18. Imagine yourself in heaven's courtroom and you have the full and undivided attention of

the highest Judge in the universe. He is looking at you, gently smiling, and He is

listening to your every word. How would you present your case? _____

_____

_____

19. Do you feel fasting changes the situation or the person most? _____ If God is

at work in both the situation and the person, what do you think is God's primary

concern? _____ Describe a situation in which both you and the situation

changed. _____ Describe a situation in which

you changed more. _____

20. Has God ever spoken to you through His Word when you were reading the Bible during

a period of fasting and prayer? _____ What lesson(s) did you learn? _____

21. If prayer is wrestling, how does the weakened condition of fasting enable us to pray more effectively? _____

   Write about a time when you were weak physically, but especially strong spiritually.

   _____

   How were the lessons you learned in that experience worth the "price" you paid? _____

   _____

22. What would happen to Christians if they were to all conduct themselves as though God really was moved to action by our fasting? _____

   _____ Why do

   you feel fasting is unpopular? _____

23. What was the most significant thing you learned in this chapter? _____

   _____

   How will that influence your Christian living from now on? _____

   _____

HABIT SIX

Handle Crises Constructively

———————⋙•◦•⋘———————

1. What was the crisis in your life that you thought about the most as you read the chapter on growing through crises? _____ _____ Did you learn anything then? _____ As you look back on it now, what advantage can you glean from reinterpreting that experience? _____ Even though time has passed since then, how can you redeem the suffering experienced then by making it work for you now as a learning experience? _____ _____ _____

2. Describe the aspect of your attitude that God wanted to change when He allowed you to experience your crisis? _____ Why did you need to change that? _____ Have you had any repeat lessons from God on that same theme? _____ _____ How did the pressure of your crisis prepare you for the change God wanted to make in your life? _____ _____

3. Read Luke 9:51. What does this verse tell us about Jesus' ability to persevere? _____ _____

   What aspect of this example of Jesus being resolute can be an encouragement to us today? _____

4. This chapter discussed the advantage of making decisions ahead of time about how to react to a crisis. How does handling problems with the rational part of us help us when emotions are too strong for us to make good decisions?_____

_____

_____

Describe an experience in which you kept cool under pressure because you had thought ahead of time about what you would do? _____

_____

5. What character flaws or weakness did God work on when you had your most recent crisis? _____ How did He show you what He was trying to do in your life?_____

In what ways have you made progress since then? _____

_____

6. Read Phil.2:8. If Jesus had to deliberately humble himself to be obedient to death on a cross, what does that suggest our attitude should be?_____

_____

In what ways are you more like Jesus now than before your life-changing crisis?_____

_____

In what ways are you more ready for your next crisis?_____

_____

7. If God has sovereign control in every situation, how does this understanding help you endure a crisis? _____

_____

What advantage does the Christian therefore have? _____

_____

8. Describe several other biblical examples, besides the crucifixion of Christ, which show

that God uses unfair situations to test and develop us. _____

_____

_____

Regardless of whether your crisis is "fair" or "unfair," how can you see that God was at

work in your experience? _____

_____

9. Read I Pet. 2:18–23, 3:17 and 4:12-13. How do those verses provide encouragement to

someone who is suffering a crisis? _____

_____

_____

_____

What experience have you had with this kind of suffering? _____

_____

10. Identify in your own words how crises provide the pressure to make us more willing to

change? _____

Describe a crisis situation you know of wherein someone would not change even when

God was helping them be willing to change._____

_____

How could that person have reacted that would have produced a good result from the

crisis?_____

_____

11. One of "temptation's" possible meanings is a "test." Read I Cor. 10:13 and I Pet. 1:6 - 7.

Based on these verses, make two positive statements about how a test or crisis can work

for good. _____

_____

_____

Make two negative statements about how a test can produce a bad effect if we do not respond correctly._____

_____

12. In your value system, is comfort or growth more important to you, why, and with what result? _____

_____

_____

How does that choice effect your attitude toward suffering? _____

_____

13. Comment on experiences you have had with wrestling, travailing, intense praying, and intercession as you struggled through your crisis._____

_____

How did God hold you steady? _____

What did God do to help you persevere?_____

_____

14. Read La. 3:27 - 33. What do these verses teach about attitude for one who is undergoing suffering? _____ What does it say about humility and its results? _____ What does it teach about God's concern for the sufferer? _____

_____

15. What kind of Christian character development has taken place in the difficult times you have faced? _____

What will you do on this point if another crisis comes to you? _____

_____

Write a three part plan for how you will (or will not) react when you face your next crisis. _____

16. What was your most important discovery in this chapter? _____

_____

How will it effect your responses to crises in the future? _____

_____

How will you help others who face crises? _____

_____

HABIT SEVEN

Know Who You Are (And Aren't)

———➤•◆•◄———

1. Read Gen. 2:7, Job 31:15; 33:6, and Is. 44:2. Write down what you believe about the individual attention God gives to the creation of each person He creates. _____ _____ What value is it to you to know that God created you just the way you are?_____ _____ _____

2. Do you dream about becoming something better than you were or are? _____ _____ Is your dream reasonable? _____ How can you keep your dreams within reason? _____ How should we balance reason and imagination when we dream of doing great things for God?_____ _____

3. What differences are there between the self you know you are and the self you would like to be? _____ How can you practically plan to become the self you want to become? _____ _____ What hindrances must you overcome? _____ _____

4. What differences are there between the self you think you are and the self you think others see in you? _____ _____

What efforts should you make to try to discover the self others really see as opposed to the self you thought others saw? _____

_____What advantage to you would there be in your learning from someone else's critique of you? _____

_____

5. In what ways have your friends helped you understand yourself better? _____

_____

In what ways can you imagine God's high aspirations for you?_____

_____

How have God's dreams for you encouraged you to aim higher?_____

_____

6. Read Heb.4:12 & 13. Name a time when you "saw yourself" in the mirror of the Bible.

_____ How did God's Word penetrate into your inner being and show you your motives? _____

_____ What development in your character occurred because of your discovery about yourself? _____

_____

7. Read Rom. 12:2. How does this verse help us resist worldly peer pressure? _____

_____

In what way does godly peer pressure work to our advantage? _____

_____ What responsibility does one Christian have to help another see blind spots and develop in Christian character?_____

_____

Compare the value of friends' opinions and God's opinions of us. _____

_____

8. Gen. 37, 39 - 48, & 50 focuses on the life of Joseph and illustrates a man with a dream

from God. Joseph could have benefited from listening to someone else since only after rigorous training did his dream come true. How did God's dream for Joseph eventually come true? _____

How could Joseph have avoided bragging?_____

How might Joseph have had both humility and a dream?_____

_____

9. Read Rom. 15:20 and I Thess. 4:11. Make a comparison between Paul's ambition for himself and his instruction about what his readers should make their ambition. _____

_____

_____

Comment on your godly ambition and explain how it compares with either of these verses. _____

_____

10. Explain why God's standard for success is different for every person._____

_____

_____

Explain why merely measuring accomplishments is a shallow way to measure success.

_____

Explain what talents or opportunities you have that help you reevaluate your own accomplishments and success._____

_____

11. Read I Cor. 3:10-15 and Eph. 6:7 & 8. Explain why the motive with which we serve is so important. _____ Explain why some services rendered by Christians may receive no reward in heaven._____

_____

_____

Express in your own words what you believe is the greatest difference between man's definition of success and God's. _____

_____

12. Read Mt. 6:3, 4, 6, 17, & 18. Explain why some people already have their reward for good things they have done. _____

_____

Explain why comparisons between yourself and others only leads to either pride or failure to appreciate your value. _____

_____

Explain why comparisons between people with differing talents and opportunities are not only unnecessary but also unwise._____

_____

13. Read Rom 12: 3-8, I Cor. 12, Eph. 4:11 and I Tim. 4:14. Why did God give different gifts, talents, and abilities to each of us?_____

_____

Write down several advantages of identifying your gifts and abilities._____

_____

What advantages are yours if you know what your own personal mission is? _____

_____

14. If you have never written a personal mission statement, write down three to six items you would want to include. _____

_____

Describe the difference between doing something good and doing what is best. _____

_____

How would a mission statement help you define what is best for you? _____

_____

15. What did you learn in this chapter that will be the greatest help to someone you know?

How will you share this idea with them? _____

What discovery was the most important to you?_____

HABIT EIGHT

Grow in Character as Your Marriage Grows

———➤•◀———

1. Compare Gen. 2:24, Mt. 19:5 & 6, and Eph. 5:31. What culture was Moses addressing when he wrote Genesis? _____ What culture was Jesus addressing when He spoke the words recorded in Mt? _____ What culture was Paul addressing when he wrote Ephesians? _____ What lesson can you draw from noting that God's instructions to all three different cultures were the same? _____ _____ How applicable is the biblical emphasis on the marriage union to all cultures? _____ _____

2. What are some of the benefits for the marriage relationship in applying the golden rule found in Mt. 7:12? _____ _____

   How does a positive reciprocal cycle—the exchange of complements and encouragement—contribute to growth in marriage? _____ _____

   How does a negative reciprocal cycle—exchanging cutting and belittling remarks— impact the marriage relationship? _____ _____

3. Read Heb. 13:7 and Eph. 6:2. The Bible tells us in these verses to consider the outcome of the lives of our leaders and to honor parents—our family's leaders. We can honor parents without duplicating every aspect of their behavior. What aspect of your parents'

example do you want to follow? _____

_____

_____

What aspect of your parents' example do you not want to follow? _____

_____

What will you have to do personally to be able to honor your parents without following

those aspects in their examples which seem flawed—after all they are human? _____

_____

4. Read Mt.7:1. How does finding the strength hidden in a weakness in a marriage partner

   fulfill this commandment?_____

   _____

   Read Phil. 2:3. How does finding the strength of a marriage partner fulfill this

   commandment? _____

   Read I Cor. 13:6 & 7. How does finding the strength, instead of criticizing the weakness,

   of a married partner match these verses?_____

   _____

5. Read I Peter 3:7. Can you identify two instructions for husbands which seem to call

   upon husbands to treat their wives well? Name them. 1. _____

   _____ 2. _____

   By saying "heirs with you" what else is Peter saying regarding the relationship between

   husband and wife?_____

   According to the last phrase of the verse, what will happen to husband's prayers if they

   will recognize these three things? _____

   _____

6. Read Gen. chapter 20 which records God's miraculous protection for Sarah when her

   husband—the great man of faith—made a mistake. Read also I Pet. 3:1 - 6 which gives us some New Testament commentary on that Old Testament story. What blessings do wives receive if they put I Pet. 3:1-6 into effect? _____

_____

Do you personally know of any contemporary examples of God caring for, protecting, or blessing submissive wives? _____

What do you feel are circumstances in which a wife is justified to separate from her husband? _____

7. Do you believe that "Submit to one another out of reverence for Christ" (Eph 5:21) applies to husbands too? _____Why? _____ What happens when husbands do not have a submissive cooperative attitude? _____

_____

Does being submissive—cooperative—take away from the manliness of the husband? _____ Why or why not? _____

8. Read Eph. 4:15. How does this scripture apply to Christian marriage partners when it comes to confronting each other for the sake of character growth? _____

_____

Read Gal. 6:1 & 2. How can the application of these verses be helpful when a marriage partner confronts a spouse for the sake of character growth? _____

_____

_____

9. Read I Cor. 11:3 and Eph. 5:23. These verses tell us that Christ is the head of the man and the head of the Church. Does Christ's headship include "lording it over" or "responsibility for the well-being of?" _____

How do you feel husbands can best follow Jesus' example of caring headship? _____

_____

10. Eph 4:31 and Heb. 12:15 says to "get rid of all bitterness" and "see to it . . . that no bitter

root grows up . . ." Do you feel marriage partners violate the principles of these verses if they allow grudges in one area of their relationship to carry over and spoil other healthy areas? _____ Explain your views on this point _____

_____

11. Eph 4:26 requires Christians to daily rid themselves of grudges, anger, or bitterness. How would you apply this to the marriage relationship? _____

_____

What special application might Eph. 4:32 have to the marriage relationship? _____

_____

12. Rom 14:19 was written for all believers, not just for marriage partners, but what special meaning might this verse have if it were to be the motto spouses followed in resolving conflict? _____

II Cor 13:11 was also written for all believers. When applied to the marriage union, what special meaning does it take on? _____

_____

13. Read Ecc. 4:9 - 12 and I Samuel 14: 6 - 14. In the latter reference we find a word picture of two unified soldiers accomplishing a great task and winning a great victory for God's people. What similarities can you see between that "picture" and a "picture" of two spouses praying, partnering, and working together to accomplish something far bigger than either of them could do on their own? _____

_____

14. Mt. 6:33 is a wonderful verse. Do you feel it is possible that "all these things" could include marital happiness, intimate joys, and blessings in your marriage, family, and home if you seek God's kingdom—God's rule in your life—first? _____ Explain your views. _____

_____

If your marriage is not like that, would you consider asking God to open your heart to visions of an improvement in this area? _____

15. What was the most important discovery you made in this chapter? _____

_____

What will you do to make use of this new truth? _____

_____

Do you feel you could share this truth with someone else and it would benefit them as well? _____ How would you share it? _____

_____

HABIT NINE

Raise Confident Children

———————

1. Read Psalms 127:3 - 5. Comment on the value God places on having children. _____

   _____

   _____

   What influences in contemporary society have caused many to have a different view of

   children? _____

   _____

2. Read I Tim. 3:4 & 5. Paul tells Timothy that managing one's family well is a

   requirement or qualification for those who want to be leaders in the church. In addition

   to providing a standard for the selection of church leaders, what do you feel these verses

   tell us about the importance of raising children well? _____

   _____

   Think about the relationship between public leadership in the church and private

   leadership in the home. Is "private" leadership in the home a purely personal thing that

   has nothing to do with qualifications for public ministry? _____

   Why or why not?_____

   _____

3. Comment on your inner reaction to observing confident, well behaved children

   compared to your reaction to observing children who were neither confident nor

   obedient. _____

   _____

4. God is God, Creator, the Almighty Potentate, and sovereign Ruler of the universe. He is also our Father and in many respects shows us by His example how we parents should raise our children. What does it mean to you that God relates to us as parent rather than as chief executive officer or president of a corporation? _____

   _____

   Why is it difficult to think of God as both a loving parent and a firm judge?_____

   _____

   How can these two roles work together?_____

   _____

5. Does God in His parental role hesitate to make rules, require obedience, and punish for disobedience? _____ Is He any less a loving parent because of his role as firm Judge? _____ How is it possible for humans to both love Him as a Father and fear displeasing the Judge? _____

   _____

   How is it possible for human parents to also fulfill these two roles to their children?

   _____

6. Read Mt. 16:27 and I Thess. 1:5-10. Does God offer both rewards and punishment in His desire to lead us to make good choices? _____ Does God make good on both kinds of promise? _____ How and when does He reward like He promised? _____
   _____ How and when does He punish like He promised?

   _____

7. How does being rewarded for obedience add to our confidence? _____

   _____

   How does God bless us with clear boundaries? _____

   _____ How can we bless our children with clear boundaries and rewards for obedience so they too will grow to be confident adults?

8. Read Eph. 6:4 and Col. 3:21. How does this verse indicate that parents should respect their children? _____

   _____

   What happens when parents push their children too hard or too far? _____

   _____

   How does this effect the friendship that could develop between parents and children?

   _____

9. The last half of Eph. 6:4 says "bring them up in the training and instruction of the Lord." Do you feel it is wise for parents to answer questions their children ask? _____ How can parents create an atmosphere wherein children feel free to approach their parents with questions? _____

   _____

10. Does training and instruction mean that parents should always be in control of the instruction agenda? _____ Can you think of instances where children's questions or the answers to children's questions are an important part of the "training and instruction in the Lord" parents should give their children? _____

    _____

    In what instances might children themselves know the subjects they need to know about so they can deal with real problems in their generation? _____

    _____

11. What does Eph 5:15 & 16 say to you about the use of time? _____

    _____

    How does this apply to your use of time with your children? _____

    _____

    What does Mt. 6:19-21 say to you about the use of time with your children? _____

What adjustment do you want to make in the amount of time you invest in your children? _____

12. Name the eights aspects of wisdom that comes from heaven, described in James 3:17.

_____

_____

As a practical biblical model for parents, how can those eight points assist you to create an atmosphere for lots of free talking and value sharing between yourself and your children over the years?_____

_____

Identify three ways that you can personally become a more child-friendly teacher and parent? _____

_____

13. How does Eph. 6:4 and Col. 3:21 help parents release their teenaged children? _____ What can you do to begin to allow your teenagers the freedom they need to learn from their own mistakes? _____ What will you do (and not do) to allow them to learn from those mistakes without their feeling "put down" by you their parent?_____

_____

14. Proverbs 22:6 in the Amplified translation reads as follows: "Train up a child in the way he should go and in keeping with his individual gift or bent, and when he is old he will not depart from it." The individual giftings of each child being different, and often different from the giftings and aspirations of their parents, provides parents with the need to lay aside their own aspirations for their children and find out what God made them to be. How can you better release and help your children to become what God

wants them to be? _____

_____

_____

15. What is the most important discovery you made while reading chapter nine and studying these study questions? _____

_____

What is your plan to put these ideas into practice? _____

_____

HABIT TEN

Raise Obedient Children

———————⟫·◦·⟪———————

1. Read Heb. 12:5-11. How does God's Word make a connection between love and discipline? _____ What does God's Word say about discipline being painful? _____

   _____

   What is the status of someone who is not disciplined? _____
   What does the Bible say about the period of time during which it is appropriate for parents to discipline children—does it last forever? _____ What is the pleasing result of discipline according to this section of Hebrews? _____

   _____

2. Read Ps. 19:14. It is not enough that the behavior of our children is right; their attitude should be too. What does Psalm 19:14 and other verses throughout the Bible suggest about correct attitude? _____

   _____

   Pride, complaints, and hatred are all matters of attitude, each forbidden by scripture. How can parents teach proper attitude as well as proper behavior? _____

   _____

3. Read Gen. 2:24. How does the unity of the married couple contribute to the strength of behavioral boundaries for children? _____

   _____ Read Proverbs 22:28. Do you think this could refer to more boundaries than just property lines? _____ Comment on the advantages of clear behavior boundaries. Are boundaries consistent with the teachings of the Bible and the way God deals with His children? _____

_____

4. Read Mt. 5:37, II Cor. 1:17. What does the Bible's teaching that a person's "yes" should mean "yes" have to do with promises of reward or punishment? _____

_____

Does this apply to rules parents make for children? _____ Promises of rewards?
_____ Promises of punishment? _____

5. When parents do not keep these kinds of promises to their children what happens to parental authority? _____ When parents keep these kinds of promises what happens to parental authority? _____

_____

6. How does the clarity with which God defines what behavior is acceptable and unacceptable hint that earthly parents too ought to be clear in their expectations? _____

_____

Explain your response. _____

Do you feel it is fair to require obedience only of those rules that have already been defined? _____ Explain your response. _____

_____

7. Do you feel any purpose is served by punishing children in front of others? _____ Is it preferred to do this privately? _____ What efforts will it require for you to begin to consistently teach, correct, and punish under control and in a private place?_____

_____

_____

8. What emotion(s) does God feel when we disobey? _____

_____ For children of God who deeply love Him, does God's

anger or God's sorrow at our disobedience more strongly motivate us to obey Him? _____ How can we use sorrow to create a similar motivation to obey on the part of our children? _____

9. Read John 5:14 and 8:34 - 35. The Bible teaches personal accountability for sin. How can this important truth be taught children when parents are dealing with punishable offences? _____

_____

Parents are God's representatives to do for children what God later does directly for them Himself. How does asking questions like "Who made the mistake?", "Who says I am to punish you?", and "Why am I punishing you?" reinforce accountability to God?

_____

_____

10. How do Pr. 19:18 and Heb. 12:11 contribute to our understanding of how or why a good parent will punish? _____

_____

How do you interpret Pr. 22:15? _____

_____

11. How can telling children in advance the number of swats they will receive be a contribution to the justice and fairness of the correction process? _____

_____

How can the use of a neutral instrument be helpful to the over-all relationship-building and correction process? _____

_____

12. The Bible has practical wisdom applicable to many situations. Read Pr.13:24 & 19:18. What does this say about punishment of disobedient children? _____

_____

Do you feel it is consistent with biblical principles to show affection to children after punishment? _____ Do you feel it is wise to pray with children so that they can avoid future errors and punishments? _____

13. How is easing off on punishments during the teenage years consistent with the biblical instruction to fathers to not embitter their children so that they become discouraged?

_____

14. Reread I Tim. 3:4 & 5. Some people seem to believe that loving control of the family is merely a qualification for spiritual leadership so the church has a way to determine who should be church leaders. But this scripture also implies that maintaining loving control of the family (also a qualification for spiritual leadership) is really right for all parents. What do you feel about this?_____

_____

_____

15. What is the most important discovery you made in this chapter?_____

_____

How will you begin to implement it? _____

_____

How will you approach your spouse or children to implement these changes? _____

_____

_____

HABIT ELEVEN

Understand Personal Finance

———⟫•⟪———

1. Read Mt. 6:19-21 & 24, Rom. 13:8, Col. 3:1 & 2, and I John 2:15-17. Can you identify several things in these verses we are to love? _____

    _____

    Identify several things in these verses we are not to love._____

    _____

    How does a value system based on these verses prepare us to reject materialism, stay out of debt, and invest carefully in those causes that support the extension of the Kingdom of God? _____

    _____

2. Read I Tim. 6:3-10. How do some Christians violate these verses? _____

    _____

    How have these verses helped to shape your value system? _____

    _____

3. Read James 2:1-5. How do these verses work against the usual way people evaluate the worth of others?_____

    _____

    What subtle ways have you tried to appear to be doing right but actually harbored feelings of favoritism? _____

    _____

4. Read Ps. 35:27, Pr. 10:22, and III John 2. These verses are sometimes used to indicate

that God wants us to prosper materially. How can we balance the verses in questions 2 & 3 that argue against seeking material prosperity with these verses that seem to indicate God's desire for material prosperity even while we are alive on earth? _____

_____

_____

What experiences and/or Bible verses can you think of that would help someone develop a balanced theology of prosperity? _____

_____

5. Read I Cor. 15:19. How does this verse contribute to a balanced theology of prosperity?

_____

How does Christian maturity contribute to our ability and willingness to defer gratification, be better stewards, and do without some things in this life? _____

_____

_____

6. How is a non-Christian materialist intellectually more consistent in loving material things than a Christian who loves material things? _____

_____

What do you need to do in order to bring your practice into conformity with a biblical (non-materialistic) value system? _____

_____

7. Read Mt. 6:1-5, 16-18. How does envisioning our heavenly account balance help us re-order our priorities? _____

_____

What adjustments would you like to make in your heavenly portfolio as a result of rethinking the issue of investing in eternal things? _____

_____

8. Read Ps. 56:8 and Phil. 3:10. How does God's record of our tears and sufferings comfort us in our present difficulties?_____

_____

Do you feel that all tears qualify to be recorded in heaven? _____ What kind of tears perhaps will not be rewarded? _____ What tears have you shed for the cause of Christ or because you value things eternal more than temporary things for which you feel you will be rewarded?_____

_____

9. Read Mt. 6:21. What do you count as treasures in your life? _____

_____ Can you give a personal illustration of something you treasure that you think about occasionally? _____

_____ Does that experience indicate that you think about what you treasure—that "where your treasure is there your heart will be also?" _____

_____

10. Was there any surprise in your own responses to the above question? _____ Do you believe your personal value system is what you want it to be? _____ What changes would you like to make, if any?_____

_____

11. Read Pr.6:6-8 and 13:11. Were you aware that the Bible deals so much with personal economic issues? _____ What is the wisdom involved in humans following the example of ants regarding savings? _____ What change might you make in your own savings pattern so it conforms to the Bible pattern? _____

_____

12. Read Acts. 24:25, Gal. 5:23, I Thess. 5:6, I Pet. 4:7 & 5:8, II Pet. 1:6. Can you see how the fruit of the Spirit of self-control impacts many different aspects of our lives?

_____ How does this include saving, spending, and choices we make about money?_____

_____

_____

Can you see how that staying in control of our money can help us avoid debt, have money when we need it, and be more intentional in saving it? _____

13. Read Pr. 13:11, 20:21 and I Cor. 16:1 & 2. Why is it better to gather money a little at a time rather than win the big prize? _____

_____ Why does the Bible emphasize

being systematic with our savings and our giving?_____

_____

14. How do you apply Rom. 13:8 and II Cor. 8:12 to the question of what to do when you want to give in an offering but don't have anything to give?_____

_____

Do you believe financial investments in God's work on earth enables Christians to lay up treasures for themselves in heaven? _____

15. In this chapter two streams of thought have been considered: (1) not loving the temporary things in this world's materialistic system, but rather loving and valuing things eternal and (2) staying out of debt rather than borrowing (by using credit cards) and saving and eventually investing money systematically. Comment on the connection between these two streams of thought. Why should it be easier for the Christian—with a strong hope for eternal things—to have a financial advantage here in earthly life as well?

_____

16. In what ways does the student of the Bible have an advantage when it comes to personal fiscal policy and practice? _____

What was the biggest surprise you had in interacting with the material in this chapter?

What changes will occur in your financial situation as a result of rethinking your financial policy in the light of the teachings of the Bible? _____

_____

HABIT TWELVE

Enjoy Physical Health for Spiritual Reasons

1. Read Jer. 9:23,24, Rom. 16:27, I Cor. 1:31, II Cor. 10:17 and Eph. 1:12 & 14. These, plus a host of other verses lead us to believe our chief purpose is to glorify God. How might this include not only what we do with our physical bodies but also care for our physical bodies? _____
Read I Tim. 4:8. Does this verse say training in godliness has greater value than physical training? _____ Does that mean that physical training has no value? _____

2. Read I Cor. 6:18 - 20. Usually I Cor. 6:18 - 20 is used to emphasize that we should not be sexually immoral. That is, in fact, the central teaching of those verses. However, how does the Apostle Paul, in verses 19 & 20, address the more inclusive matter of all the things we do to our bodies as well as what we do with them? _____

_____

How do you think practical matters such as diet, exercise, and rest could be included in the instruction of verse 10 & 20?_____

_____

3. Read Rom. 12:1. How do diet, exercise, and rest help us offer our bodies as living sacrifices to God? _____

_____

How does good physical appearance bring glory to God? _____ Do you feel physical appearance includes posture, care for hair, personal grooming, and staying in good physical condition as well as the clothes we put on them? _____ Explain your

71

views._____

_____

4. Read I Sam. 16:7. In the first part of that verse, God told Samuel not to look on Eliab's appearance. Usually we use this incident in scripture to emphasize the importance of the condition of the heart before God, and that is the central truth to be learned. However, can you see a second lesson also implied? _____ Does our physical appearance give an impression? _____ Should Christians try as much as possible to give a good impression in both their physical appearance and the inner beauty of the heart? _____ Is there any reason not to include both aspects and glorify God both ways? _____ Explain your views. _____

_____

5. In addition to the appearance issue discussed above, what do you think about our bodies as a temporary machine which with care, maintenance, and wise stewardship can last longer, feel better, and produce more service for kingdom-related causes? _____ From a biblical standpoint, is stewardship of our bodies also a possible spiritual reason to maintain physical health? _____ Explain your views. _____

_____

6. Read Ex. 20 8-11. Of all the ten commandments, why do you feel this is the longest?

_____

Write down a few of the details of this commandment that have the most meaning to you. _____

_____

What short-range advantages can you think of for keeping this commandment?

_____

What long-range advantages? _____

7. In addition to the command to rest one day a week, do you feel this commandment also includes the command that we are to work six days—even though our employment may require fewer than six days? _____

    Is the principle of this commandment still fulfilled when you rest another day other than Sunday? _____ How does it take faith to rest—especially when we are anxious to accomplish something? _____

    Do you have the faith in God you need to "lie down in green pastures" (Ps 23:2) even when there is much work to do? _____

8. What kind of activity do you do on your job? _____ What activity do you like to do that is different from your work that leaves you rested? _____

    How does Ps. 127:2 reinforce the commands in God's Word to rest properly? _____

9. Can you think of ways that not only you, but also your family, would benefit from you taking a day each week to rest? _____

    What events in your childhood can you recall that seem to reinforce the benefit to the whole family for the parents in the family to regularly take a day for rest? _____

    What vacation in your childhood contributed to the pleasure and good memories of your family life?_____

10. Read Ecc. 2:24. This verse was addressed to an agrarian society where work and

exercise were essentially the same thing. Do you find a biblical encouragement to exercise in this verse? _____ Read Ps. 139:14. How does the body's ability to respond well to exercise demonstrate a part of what this verse means? _____

_____

11. What exercise makes you feel good? _____ What exercise fits most conveniently into your weekly schedule? _____

_____

If you were convinced that God wanted you to enjoy that exercise would you do it more regularly? _____ Is it possible that God wants you to enjoy that exercise? _____

12. Read Rom. 14:20 and Ph. 3:18 & 19. What rules have you made for yourself so that you enjoy foods God has provided for our enjoyment and at the same time you do not make your stomach your god? _____

_____

What rules have you made for yourself regarding eating nutritional food versus eating food that is stimulating, convenient, or pleasant but not so nutritional? _____

_____

Is there anything about your eating habits that needs to be reconsidered? _____ If so, what? _____

13. Read Ex. 12:35 and Luke 16:1 - 9. Moses told the Israelites to use the Egyptians treasures and Jesus commended the dishonest manager because he had acted shrewdly. Could the use that Christians make of things in the non-Christian world include not just material things but also ideas—providing they are not unbiblical? _____ Can Christians use secular ideas about health, rest, and exercise for a spiritual purpose and glorify God? _____ Is God pleased if you benefit from reading a book about health and as a result begin to enjoy greater health? _____ In what ways have the ideas in this chapter challenged you to strive for physical health for spiritual

reasons? _____

_____

14. From your knowledge of Scripture, make a comparison between over-drinking and over-eating. _____ Do you feel your philosophy toward what you eat is as important as your attitude toward what and how much you drink or even whether or not to drink? _____ Can you see an inconsistency in being concerned about drinking issues and careless about eating issues? _____ Does this line of thought require you to reevaluate either your drinking or eating habits? _____

5. Read Pr. 17:22. What practical change can you make in your life habits to bring more health-giving joy into your life? _____

_____

What anxiety do you need to cast on the Lord so that your "crushed spirit" does not have a negative effect on your physical health?_____

_____

What positive effect has your joy, freedom, and sense of forgiveness in Jesus Christ had on your sense of well-being and physical health?_____

_____

16. What has been the greatest surprise to you in this chapter? _____

_____

List several ways this discovery might benefit your friends? _____

_____

List several ways to share these ideas with your "group" of friends to encourage each other to enjoy physical health and good appearance as a means of glorifying God with your bodies?_____

_____

HABIT THIRTEEN

Grasp the Bigger Picture

1. Read Rom. 8:16,17. It is an amazing and mysterious thing to consider that we are co-heirs with Jesus. Do you think of yourself as a partner with God in His great work? _____ What do you think of first when you think of yourself as a co-worker or partner with Jesus? _____ What project is God up to that you would like to be a part of? _____

   _____

2. Read Gen. 1:1 & 2, glance over Gen. 10 and read Gen 11:1-9. Early civilizations recorded only the story of their own nations' mythology. The Jews' Scriptures, however, recorded points of interest regarding the whole earth, all nations, languages, and ethnic groups. What does this tell us about the God of the Jews? _____

   _____

   What are the implications of a Bible with a world-wide scope?_____

   _____

   What effect does such a scope have on Christians' concern for missions and world evangelism? _____

   _____

3. Apart from the Christ-like manners and demeanor Christians should always demonstrate, is there any difference in the disciplines, techniques, strokes, serves, and tactics of a Christian and a non-Christian tennis player? _____ Can a Christian tennis player learn how to play tennis from a non-Christian coach? _____

4. Following this same line of reasoning (assuming you said "yes" both times in the paragraph above), do you think it is scriptural to use sound business principles in administrating affairs of the Kingdom of God? _____ Is it unspiritual to study administration and management and use those ideas in administrating a missions program? _____ If there are few missionaries serving in a highly responsive area and many missionaries serving in a well-reached or unresponsive area, would it be unspiritual to move some of the missionaries to the more responsive area?_____

5. Read Deut. 6:6-9. What do these verses say about training children in the ways of the Lord? _____

As a part of training children in a Christian worldview, do you think it would be consistent with Deut. 6:6-9 for Christian parents to read Bible stories, missionary stories, and other Christian stories to young children? _____ What can you do in a way that would be interesting and understandable, to increase your children's awareness of the importance of world evangelism? _____

_____

6. Read Hebrews chapter eleven. This chapter tells us about a great host of heroes and heroines of the faith. Chapter 12 calls them a "great cloud of witnesses." These two chapters hint that there may be other historical figures in the history of the church and missions from whom we might learn spiritual lessons. Explain your views about reading Bible stories, church history, and missions history for illustrations of Christian heroism?

_____

_____

How can you use your thoughts on this subject to pass on to the next generation an awareness of missionary work in the world?_____

_____

7. What is your view about using modern technology to advantage in gospel work?

Is there anything unspiritual about using technology in God's work? _____

8. Read Acts 13:36. This verse tells of what hero of faith who served his generation and then passed on? _____ Do you see a suggestion here that each person is to serve his generation? _____ Are the challenges and opportunities of all generations the same? _____ What unique challenges or opportunities do you have in your generation? _____

How do you intend to rise to those challenges and seize those opportunities?_____

9. Read I Sam. chapter one and the first eleven verses of chapter two. What can we learn from the joy with which Hannah gave her son to God's service? _____

Samson's and John the Baptist's parents also raised their children and dedicated them to the work of God. What biblical value do you see in these stories which could be an encouragement to parents today to raise their children to serve God in the next generation? _____

10. Everything we do we do for God whether we offer our time, work, or money. How might offering our children to God's service fit in this context?_____

How might raising our children well—preparing them—be a part of this? _____

Write several similarities between offering money and offering children to God. _____

11. Read Romans 8:15. What can you do in your role as a parent to train your children and shift their trust toward you eventually to trust "papa" God in their generation?_____

How can you model parenthood in such a way that your children will trust their heavenly father and serve him confidently in their generation? _____

12. Read Eph. 2:10. The word "workmanship" is a translation of the Greek word, *poiema* which means something which is made. We get the English word "poem" from this Greek word. We are God's poem—a product of His highest form of craftsmanship. Compare the craftsmanship required to create the universe with the craftsmanship required to recreate a fallen person._____

Is creation or recreation easier? _____ What does the miracle of creation show us about God's power? _____

What does the miracle of recreation show us about God's love? _____

13. Read John 3:16 and I John 2:15 - 17. One verse says God "loved" and the other says we should "not love" the world. In what sense should we love the world? _____

In what sense should we not love the world? _____

Do you feel it is possible to simultaneously obey both of these principles?_____ How? _____

14. Read Rom. 15:20 where Paul describes his own ambition. Next read I Thess. 4:11 & 12

where Paul tells his readers what their ambition should be. What can you learn from these two different ambitions?_____

_____

Which of those two ambitions best describes what you feel God is telling you your ambition should be? _____ Why do you feel this way? _____

_____

15. Read Is. 52:7. How do you reconcile Isaiah's lofty description of a missionary and the physical realities of sweat, work, language and culture study, and living difficulties that go with actually serving as a missionary in a foreign context? _____

_____

Read Acts. 20:22 - 24. Paul did not hide the difficulties he faced, but neither did he let them keep him from fulfilling God's lofty purpose. How can Christians keep the lofty purpose in mind when going through the difficulties entailed in them? _____

_____

16. What was the most important discovery you made while reading and studying this thirteenth chapter? _____

What was the biggest surprise you experienced as you responded to the questions in this chapter of the Bible study guide? _____

How will you share these discoveries with your friends?_____

_____

What will you do differently in raising your children?_____

_____

Will these thoughts make it easier for you to release your children to do missions work? _____ Why or why not? _____

HABIT FOURTEEN

Become Sensitive to Contexts

———⟫•⟪———

1. When Jesus said go into all the world, do you think He included the idea of going into every person's world? _____ What is the difference between going geographically to another part of the world and going into someone's conceptual world?_____
   _____

2. Read Mt. 10:32 - 39 and John 3:1 - 3. In one of these sections (Mt. 10:32 - 39) Jesus required open confession and in the other (John 3:1 - 3) He was willing to receive an inquirer secretly and made no requirements of public confession. Why? _____
   _____

   How does John 3:1 - 3 illustrate that Jesus is willing to start with people where they are?
   _____
   _____

3. Read Mt. 2:1 - 2 and Lk. 2:8 - 15. To whom did God communicate through a star? _____ To whom did God communicate through angels? _____
   _____ How does this illustrate what missiologists call "receptor oriented communication?"_____
   _____

4. In what way has God communicated personally with you? _____
   _____

   How could you yourself become a better communicator? _____
   _____

What have you learned already in this study about communication? _____

_____

5. What is the difference between not liking a message and not understanding the message?

_____

_____

Can the communicator do anything about either of those responses—not liking it or not

getting it? _____ What can we do to help people understand the message?_____

_____

What can we do to help people like the message? _____

_____

6. Read Jer. 18:1 - 6. God took Jeremiah to a potter's house and used a material process to illustrate a spiritual truth. How do these verses illustrate God's interest in communication? _____

_____

How do these verses illustrate Jeremiah's willingness to use something the local people understood in order to communicate effectively? _____

_____

7. Read John 10:1 - 10 How do these verses illustrate Jesus' interest in communication?

_____

When Jesus' hearers did not grasp the meaning of His "figure of speech" in verse 6 what did Jesus say as He continued in verses 7 - 10? _____

_____

8. How does John 10:1 - 10 illustrate Jesus' willingness to use word pictures, symbols, and metaphors to communicate? _____

_____

Which was more important to Jesus, the meaning or the symbol that was used to express the meaning? _____ Did Jesus change the symbol in order to preserve or accurately communicate the meaning? _____ What is the supracultural meaning (the meaning that is to be applied in all cultures) Jesus was communicating in John 10: 1-10? _____

_____

9. Read Ps. 29. Does the fact that this poem originated from a heathen culture honoring Baal (a heathen god) mean that it cannot be used to glorify the true God? _____ How does the inclusion in the Bible of this adapted form of a heathen poem illustrate the importance of adapting our message so that it has impact? _____

_____

_____

10. Read Act 17:28. In Paul's address at the Areopagus what does his use of a heathen poem indicate about his desire to "connect" with his audience? _____

_____

_____

What teaching, sermon, lecture, or speech especially "connected" with you because of the good use of some poem, song, proverb, or joke from contemporary culture?

_____

What does this say about the communication process?_____

_____

_____

11. If you were a missionary to Papua New Guinea and understood the use of pigs as a means of exchange and symbol of forgiveness for debt, would you use that symbol to illustrate how Jesus purchased our forgiveness? _____ Why or why not?

_____

_____

Do you think it is acceptable to change some of the figurative language (symbol, metaphor, simile) of the gospel in order to better communicate it in another culture? __

_____

Why would some American Christians misunderstand you? _____

_____

Would it be more important to you to be understood by New Guinea people or that you avoid being misunderstood by your friends in your own home nation? _____

_____

12. If you are a youth worker, would it be more important to you to use words young people readily understood? _____ Why? _____

_____

Would you use those words even if some older people around you misunderstood you? _____ Why?_____

13. What was the biggest surprise you had while reading this chapter?_____

_____

Are you willing to experiment with words in order to increase the degree to which your listener understands your life-giving meaning?_____

How will you try to avoid possible misunderstandings?_____

_____

_____

HABIT FIFTEEN

Obey From The Heart

———⇒•◦•⇐———

1. Read John 14:23 & 24. Why did Jesus make a connection between love and obedience in

    verse 23? _____ How is the connection

    between love and obedience reinforced in verse 24? _____

    _____

    Do you think obedience to God includes obeying whatever the Holy Spirit directs a

    believer to do as well as obeying the written teachings of Jesus? _____ Why or why

    not? _____

    _____

2. Read Gen. 1:26 & 27 and 2:15-17. How do these verses suggest that God created an

    atmosphere in which man was free to use his freedom of choice to make real choices?

    _____

    _____

    What is the relationship between freedom of choice and obedience?_____

    _____

3. If there is no human freedom of choice then there is also no human personal

    responsibility—everything would be predetermined and God Himself would be

    responsible. Do you think it is possible (or fair) to be truly accountable for something

    over which you have no control? _____ Why or why not?_____

    _____

    Why is it important to understand the relationship between freedom of choice, obedience, responsibility, and accountability? _____

_____

4. Read Luke 12:47 & 48 and John 19:11. How do these verses indicate that there are

degrees of sin and implied degrees of punishment? _____

_____

How can these verses serve as a comfort to those whose ancestors or relatives have died

without knowing God? _____

_____

5. Read Mt. 21:28 - 31. How do these verses indicate that obedience can have degrees?

_____

Read I Cor. 10:31, I Thess. 5:16 & 18. How do these verses indicate that if we are not

obeying joyfully, we are not obeying fully? _____

_____

_____

Read Col. 3:23 & 24. Why should we obey joyfully, fully, and energetically? _____

_____

_____

6. Read Ps. 123:2. Can you think of anyone you know who illustrates this kind of careful,

watchful, and constant obedience? _____ How can you learn from their

example? _____

Do you think that God sometimes signals to us by circumstances He allows to come our

way what He wants us to do? _____ Write an illustration from your own life. _____

_____

_____

7. Read I Samuel 15. In this story is found the famous quotation, "To obey is better than

sacrifice." Saul was presumptuous and had other attitude problems, so it is easy to see that his "sacrifice" was not as good as obedience would have been. However, even if he had had a good attitude and wanted to add to what God had required, why could that also have been disobedience? _____

_____

How much can Christians add to the instructions God has given them and initiate service to God from their own hearts and have it fully accepted by God? _____

_____

_____

8. Read Isaiah 55:8 & 9. God is wiser than man. How does this concept effect our initiating "service" beyond God's requirements? _____

_____

Are humans always presumptuous when they initiate "service" for God? _____
Under what circumstances are Christians presumptuous to initiate service done for God?

_____

_____

Under what circumstances are Christians not presumptuous to initiate service to God?

_____

_____

What are some of the problems that might ensue from doing more than God requires?

_____

9. How do you think doing more than God requires might lead to inwardly relying on works to gain God's approval? _____ Why do you feel it is superior to simply obey what God is telling us to do than to try to do more?_____

_____

_____

10. What experience have you had of trying to do more than God required?_____

What were the results?_____

_____

Why do we sometimes unconsciously think we are wiser than God and therefore add to

His instructions? _____

_____

11. Read Deut. 10:12 & 13 and Rom. 7:12. How is keeping the Ten Commandments and

other laws of God actually good for us? _____

_____ Read Ps. 119:72. David loved

God's laws. Do you believe it is consistent to say we love God's law and simultaneously

disobey it? _____ Are you structuring your week in accord with the

commandment to rest one day a week?_____ If not, how can you change your

current schedule?_____

_____

12. In disciplining ourselves to fast, pray, keep our thoughts pure, control our gaze and

various appetites and quickly, completely, and cheerfully obey God etc., is there a

danger of becoming works oriented? _____ How can we clearly separate our thoughts

about being forgiven (receiving salvation) by grace from earning rewards by works of

obedience?_____

_____

13. Does God give both gifts (something given freely) and rewards (something earned)?

_____ Does God reward obedience? _____ How is the emphasis on self-

control, discipline, and obedience in *Habits of Highly Effective Christians* not an attempt

to maintain by works a salvation provided by grace? _____ Even with all our

appreciation for the grace of God which provides a free salvation and entrance into

God's heavenly home, there is still a place for works, discipline, self-control, obedience, service, and expectation of a promised reward. How have these thoughts affected your motivation in service to God? _____

_____

14. Explain biblically how someone can get into heaven and spend eternity there by simply believing in Jesus Christ—that salvation is not a behavioral issue. _____

_____

_____

Explain biblically how God's reward system (something quite different from obtaining salvation) is a behavioral issue. _____

_____

How has the enemy lulled us into an easy religion by causing us to wrongly emphasize grace (an appropriate emphasis when discussing salvation) in the area of Christian behavior which, according to the Bible, is the area for service, earning eternal crowns, and other rewards?_____

_____

15. Explain how obedience can help a person become all they can be. _____

_____

Why can a disobedient person never fulfill his potential?_____

_____

What do you need to begin to do to become a more highly effective Christtian?_____

_____

16. What was your biggest challenge in this chapter?_____

_____

What will help you the most as you try to become all you can be? _____

_____

What do you have to do to begin to implement that idea? _____

17. Can you list several ways you might be able to help someone else understand how they too can become more highly effective? _____

_____

Are you willing to confront and to be confronted so as to be more obedient and fulfill more of your potential? _____ With whom might you form a mutually beneficial alliance? _____

HABIT SIXTEEN

Persevere Tanaciously

———➤◦◅———

1. Read Ps. 115:3. If God really does "whatsoever pleases him," is it reasonable to believe that adversity is planned and used by God? _____ Why do you believe this way?

_____

_____

2. Describe at least one instance in which you have grown through adversity? _____

_____

Arguing from the results, how can you thank God now for that adversity? _____

_____

Can you see how adversity is a necessary part of a world in which we are developed to be our best? _____ Do you believe God is more concerned about comfort or character development? _____ Give your reason(s) for believing this. _____

_____

_____

3. Read Mt. 11:28 - 30 and Jn.15:1 & 2. How would you explain the difference in emphases in these two verses to a new Christian? _____

_____

Under what circumstances should Christians emphasize Mt. 11:28? _____

_____

Under what circumstances is it more appropriate to emphasize Jn. 15:2? _____

_____

4. Have you ever experienced adversity even when you were carefully obeying God? _____ Can Christians experience adversity even when they are in the will of God? _____ Have you ever been out of the will of God and He used adversity to bring you back into His will? _____ Does adversity happen only to those out of the will of God? _____ Does adversity happen only to those who are in the will of God? _____ What is the best way to overcoming adversity? _____

_____

_____

_____

5. Read Mark 6:45 - 52. Do you see any similarities between your adversity and that experienced by the disciples? _____ What similarities give you courage to face your storm with perseverance? _____

_____

What was your most recent storm and how did Jesus bring you through it? _____

_____

If you are still in it, what "ghost" makes it seem worse than it really is? _____

_____

6. What would happen if every time we did the will of God things went well and every time we did not do the will of God things went bad for us? _____

_____

Does God sometimes give us especially "good sailing" in order to encourage us? _____ When did God recently give you an especially encouraging and affirming experience?

_____

Will you remember it next time you experience a storm? _____

7. What does Mark 6:49 & 50 tell us about how the disciples reacted when they saw Jesus?

_____

Was their reaction consistent with who Jesus was? _____ Was their reaction consistent with who (or what) they thought they saw? _____ Do we react according to what is really happening or what we think is happening? _____ Explain why we usually react according to what we think is happening even if that is different than what is really happening?_____

8. Read Nu. 13:33, 22:4, and Josh. 2:11. What did the Israelites think they looked like in the eyes of the Canaanites? _____ What did the Canaanites really think? _____ How do you account for the difference in the perceptions of these two peoples (who were observing the very same circumstances) each of whom perceived the other to be a vastly superior foe? _____

9. How does the difference in the perceptions of Israelites and Canaanites looking at the same circumstances, illustrate that fear is more a matter of perception than circumstances?_____ _____ Do you see a common thread in the Israelites' and disciples' fear? _____ Were either of their fears justified? _____ What was the reasonable alternative to that fear? _____

10. What miracle had God just done for the Israelites that could have encouraged them? _____ What miracle had Jesus performed the day before for the disciples that could have encouraged them? _____

What are you afraid of right now? _____ How do you know your perceptions are correct? _____ Is it possible that you are not seeing it correctly? _____ What miracle did God perform for you recently from which you could draw courage to persevere through your present storm?

_____

11. Read Josh 1:6, Ps. 23:3 & 4, and John 14:16 - 18. What do the courage, restoration, and comfort promised in these verses have in common?_____

_____

How can these three things contribute to perseverance in the life of a Christian? _____

_____

Write of a time when God gave you the courage, restoration, or comfort you needed in order to persevere at a time of adversity? _____

_____

12. Read Mt. 2:1 - 11. How did the Maji overcome adversity and persevere? _____

_____

_____

How were circumstances different than they expected? _____

_____

Often others have more advantages than we—more resources, friends, contacts, talents, educations. Are you using any of these reasons (or perceptions) to excuse yourself from persevering? _____ If so, when do you intend to change your policy? _____

_____

13. How can we develop perseverance and tenacity in the children we are raising?_____ _

_____

When does our "help" weaken them? _____ When is our help appropriate? _____ What criterion do (or will) you use to determine whether to help your children for their encouragement or to allow them to work it out themselves to develop their ability to persevere?_____

_____

14. Read Heb. 11. Name three of the persons mentioned there whose example of perseverance encourages you: 1. _____ 2. _____ 3. _____ Pretend that you are the writer of that chapter and write four sentences that describe yourself. "By faith _____

_____

_____

_____

_____

15. Read Mt. 13:44. What does buying the whole field mean to you? _____

_____

What is the Lord asking you to do which for you means buying the whole field? _____

_____

16. The only reason any of us need to quit is: "It doesn't matter that much to me." Do you agree? _____ When one quits, is he, in essence, saying "It doesn't matter that much to me?" _____ What obstacle is hindering you now from pursuing your goal?

_____

Is it worth overcoming that obstacle in order to obtain your goal?_____

_____

Does it matter that much to you? _____ Will you not only decide to do the right thing, but also persevere? _____

17. Read Heb 12:2. How could Jesus find joy in the cross? _____

_____

In what way does His example challenge or encourage you to persevere?_____

_____

18. What was your biggest discovery in this chapter? _____ Will this discovery make any difference in your life? _____ If so, what difference will it

make?_____

_____

What will you do to share these ideas with your friends?_____

_____

HABIT SEVENTEEN

Be Intimate with Your Heavenly Father

—————⇒»•◦•«⇐—————

1. Read Rom. 11:33-36 and Rom. 8:15 - 17. Notice how Paul stresses two beautiful and opposing themes in verses within three chapters of each other in the book of Romans. How do you explain these two themes which occur repeatedly throughout scripture—that God is grand, glorious, great, and powerful and also near, approachable, tender, and daddy to us?_____

_____

Also Read Pr. 1:7. What images usually are associated with the "fear of the Lord?"

_____

Now compare Pr. 1:7 (which causes some to hold God at a distance) with James 4:8 which instructs us to draw near to God. How do you balance these two emphases in your times of prayer? _____

_____

2. Which of these two themes—God's greatness or approachability—was uppermost in your mind when you first came to know the Lord?_____

How long was it before you "discovered" the other side of God's character? _____

_____ Which aspect seems uppermost in your mind today?

_____

3. Mt. 6:7 says we are to avoid "babbling like pagans." What do you do to keep your mind from wandering when you pray?_____

Would calling God by a different title when you pray help make your conversation with

Him seem more real? _____ What endearing term did you use for your father (or other father figure, or mother if you were not raised by a loving father) when you felt especially close to him? Could you be comfortable calling God that? _____ Would that make your conversation with God seem more like you were talking with a personal friend? _____ Do you think God would like that? _____

_____

4. Read Lk. 12:32 and notice that Jesus includes three types of relationships in one sentence. What words would you use to explain how Pr. 18:10 where soldiers run to the safety of a tower, Mt. 18:3 & 4 where Jesus tells us to be like little children, and Mt. 23:37 where Jesus tells us he would like to gather us to the protection under his wings could all fit together?_____

_____

_____

What do mixed figures of speech teach us about God?_____

_____

What do mixed figures of speech teach us about ourselves and our relationship with God? _____

_____

5. In Jn. 15:2 Jesus says God is the Gardener who prunes us so we will be more fruitful. In Heb. 12:5-11 it says that He is the Father who corrects children He loves. How do you bring these two ideas together? _____

_____

Are you willing to experience the pruning of the Gardener or the correction of the Father for the sake of personal growth? _____

How would that process help you become a more effective Christian? _____

6. Read I Jn. 4:18. In what way does having a loving and intimate relationship with God affect your attitude toward any correction He may give you?_____

_____

_____ In what way, if any, might you adjust your prayer regarding correction and pruning so you can be more fruitful? _____

_____

7. In I Kings 18:16-46 you can find a record of Elijah's experience on Mount Carmel. Elijah did not use the old altar as it was and neither did he build a new altar. Instead, verse 30 says, he "repaired the altar of the LORD." How would you apply the symbolism of Elijah repairing an old altar to the idea of your adding new truth to old instead of throwing out all the old for the sake of learning the new? _____

_____

What old "truth" needs to be pitched out of your life to make room for any new truth you learned in this chapter about your relationship with your Father? _____

_____

What old truth needs to remain as you add new understanding? _____

_____

8. Read Rom. 12:2. Write down several ideas you feel have hindered you from viewing God in more intimate ways. _____

_____

Most people think God is far away or, if He comes near, He is a Judge or Dictator making demands we cannot keep. In what way, if any, does that "pattern of this world" influence your impression of what God is like? _____

_____

What specific aspect of God's character do you want to reconsider or change in order to better understand God's nearness? _____

_____

9. Read Ex. 20:2 – 4. In what way in our times is "bowing down" to any concept of God other than the Bible teaches similar to making images or idols and worshipping them?

_____

_____

What makes you think God wants us to be intimate with Him? _____

_____ Do we dishonor Him in any way when we think of Him as "Daddy" or any other endearing term? _____

_____

10. If your relationship with your father when you were young was not pleasant, what will you do to allow God today to be the "daddy" you never had? _____

_____

How will you overcome, or allow your heavenly Daddy to help you overcome, any memories that might hinder that process?_____

_____

If your relationship with your father when you were young was pleasant, how did that prepare you for a pleasant and intimate relationship with your heavenly Daddy?

_____

What steps will you take to insure that your children will have an easy time accepting God as their heavenly Daddy too? _____

11. What was the most important lesson you learned from this chapter?_____

_____

What new goal would you like to set for yourself based upon your reflections on this chapter? _____

_____

Printed in the United States
63931LVS00006B/26